BUMPER BOOK

Look and Find® Christmas

3 Christmas Look and Find books in 1!

Santa

The Night Before Christmas

Twelve Days of Christmas

pi kids® publications international, ltd.

The Night Before
Christmas

'Twas the night before Christmas,
and all through the city
Every creature was stirring—
the lights were so pretty!
This mouse was out searching
for Santa with care.
Couldn't risk getting squished
before I got there.

My name is A. Mouse, and
I'm out looking for Santa
downtown. Can you
spot me? Can you
help me find Santa Claus?
And while you're at it, see if
you can find these city folks.

Calvin Con Artist

Myra Meter Maid

Celia City Slicker

Peter Pickpocket

Tex, the urban cowboy

Ellen Executive

On the night before Christmas,
the mall is jam-packed.
(No St. Nick in sight—
he's still filling his sack.)
The parents are shopping,
the stuff looks entrancing.
Their kids dream of skateboards,
not sugarplums dancing!

Can you spot me, A. Mouse, and
Santa Claus, too? And can you find
these last-minute shoppers?

Winnie Whiner

Clara the Clothes Horse

Charlie Charge It

Ms. Gotbucks

Kassie Klepto

Bo the Bargain Hunter

Wanda Window Shopper

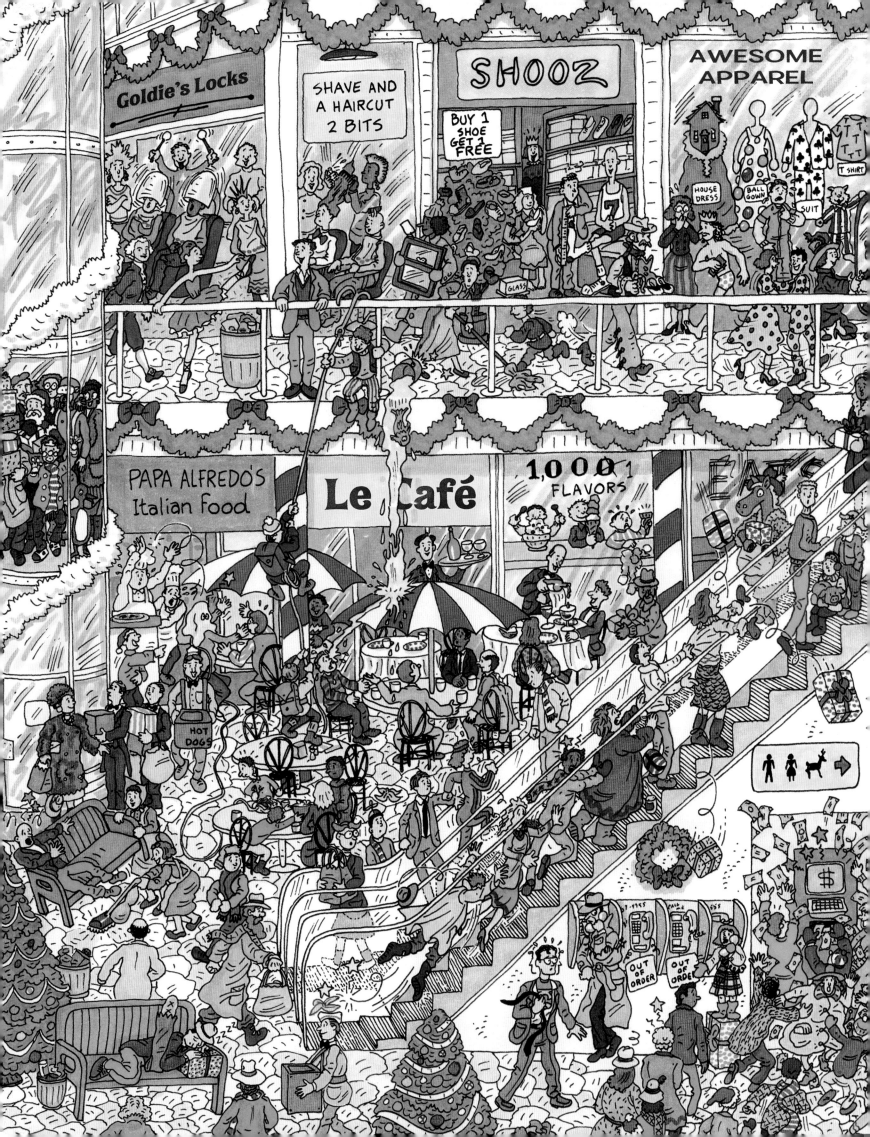

On the night before Christmas,
what do you think
Is more fun than a party
at an ice-skating rink?
The moon was so bright,
I could see I was near—
For before me I saw
eight skating reindeer!

I know I'm hot on Santa's trail—
even though it's pretty cold here!
Do you see him? And can you find
me and Santa's eight reindeer?

Dasher

Dancer

Vixen

Donder

Comet

Cupid

Prancer

Blitzen

COCOA

It's the night before Christmas,
　what do animals do?
Only one way to see;
　I sneaked into the zoo!
I know Santa is here;
　to his reindeer he's shoutin',
"To the bears in their cage!
　To the seals in the fountain!"

This party's a zoo! After you find
Santa and me, A. Mouse, see if you
can spot these unusual critters.

A Christmas seal

A silly goose

A playin' possum

A dandy lion

A holy cow

A bum steer

Leapin' lizards

A pink elephant

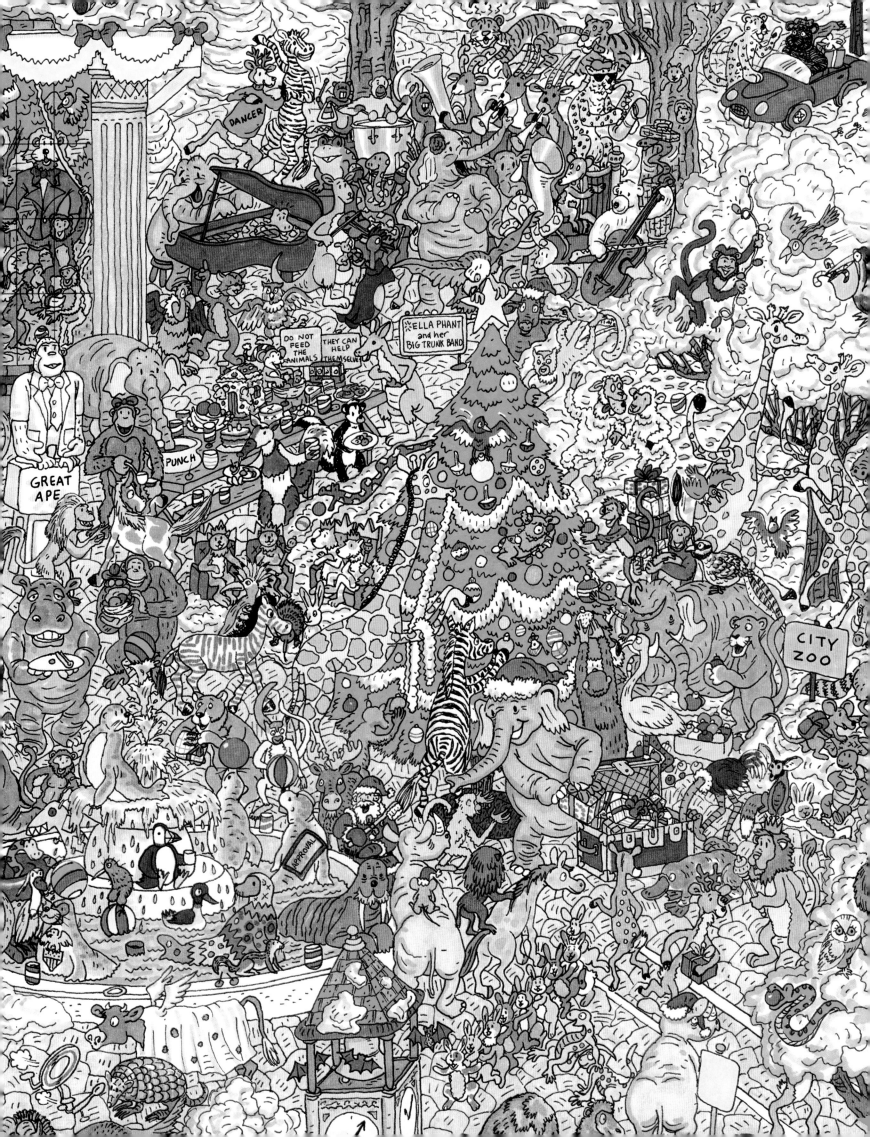

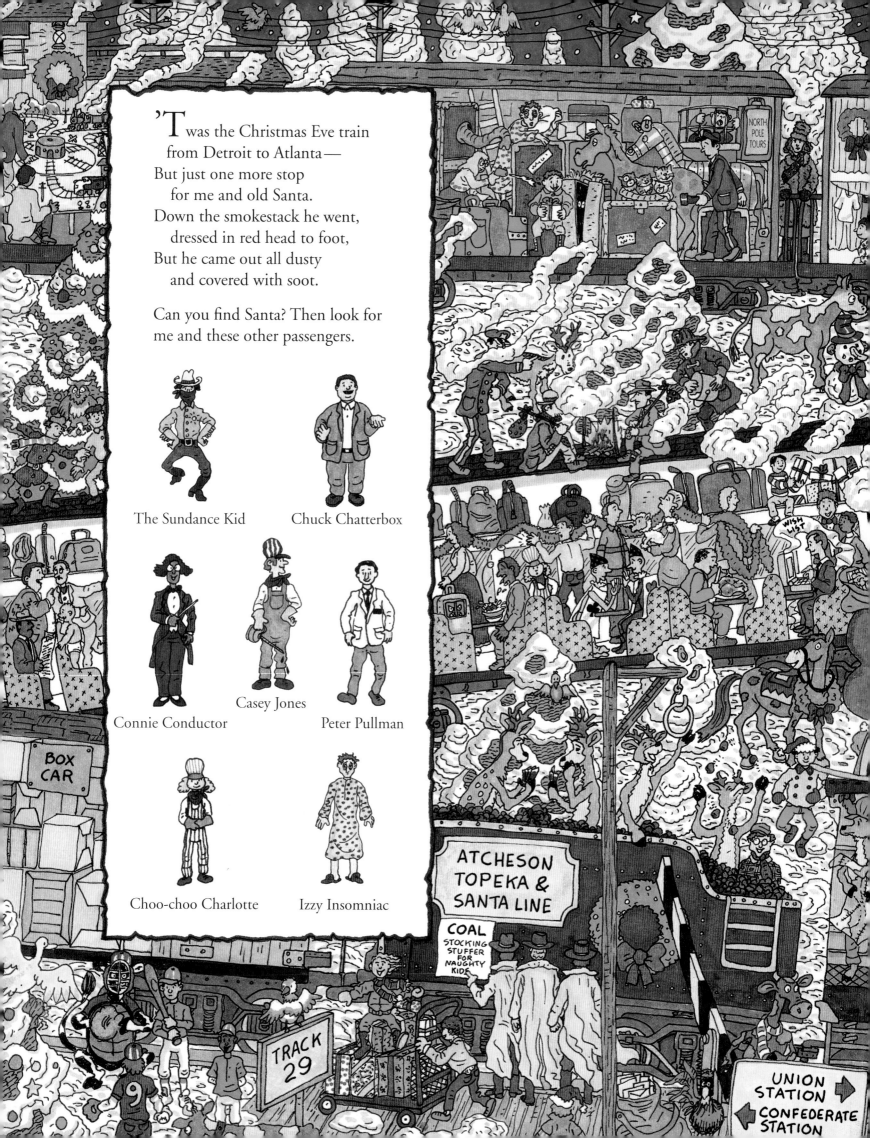

'Twas the Christmas Eve train from Detroit to Atlanta—
But just one more stop for me and old Santa.
Down the smokestack he went, dressed in red head to foot,
But he came out all dusty and covered with soot.

Can you find Santa? Then look for me and these other passengers.

The Sundance Kid

Chuck Chatterbox

Connie Conductor

Casey Jones

Peter Pullman

Choo-choo Charlotte

Izzy Insomniac

In the gingerbread factory
on Christmas Eve,
The night shift is cooking
Santa's candy to leave.
For stockings, for presents,
for St. Nick's own belly—
It's the sweets that he eats
that make it like jelly!

Sweet dreams! I'm helping myself
to a few goodies. Can you find me?
Then help me find Santa and these
workers in the gingerbread factory.

Lovely Louise

Fred Foreman

Clarisse Carpenter

Sarah Slacker

Wesley Worker

Sleepy Sam

Bill Boss

Quality Control Carol

On the night before Christmas,
Santa's elves are so busy,
Just watching them rush
is making me dizzy!
I laughed as I watched them,
in spite of myself—
It's hard to say which
is the clumsiest elf!

The elves are in such a hurry, some presents aren't coming out quite right. Can you find Santa and me? Can you find these odd presents?

An airplane

Roller skates

A stuffed animal

A tea set

A clock

A football

A doll

A hockey stick

A bicycle

On the night before Christmas,
    every school has a party.
St. Nick is there, too,
    though he is a bit tardy.
He goes straight to work
    and starts filling up stockings—
The kids are still in 'em,
    and that's what's so shocking!

Can you find Santa and me as we join in the good times? Can you help me find these school things?

A ruler

A stapler

A notebook

A blackboard

A desk

Glue

A box of crayons

A globe

'T was the night before Christmas,
   when all are asleep.
They're snug in their beds
   and they're counting their sheep.
Santa shouts as his sleigh
   disappears out of sight,
"Merry Christmas to all,
   and to all a good night!"

It's getting late, and I'm still stirring.
Can you find me and Santa? Then
help me find these bedtime things.

A bedtime story

A night-light

A nightgown

A nightcap

A pair of fuzzy slippers

A teddy bear

Six sheep for the children to count

A toothbrush

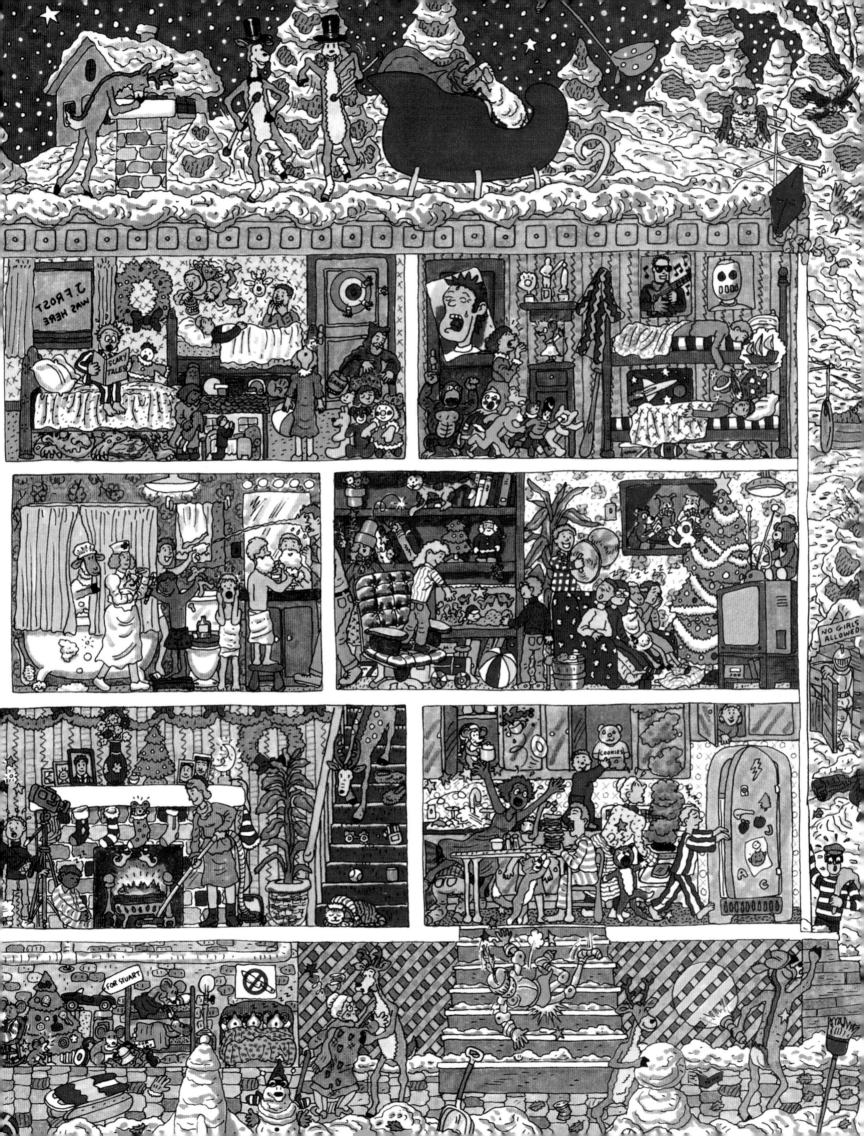

Go back to all the Night Before Christmas scenes to find even more things!

Downtown

- [ ] The Three Wise Men
- [ ] The Nutcracker
- [ ] The Little Drummer Boy
- [ ] A partridge in a pear tree
- [ ] Elves doing some Christmas "rapping"
- [ ] Mrs. Claus
- [ ] Mistletoe
- [ ] A shepherd

Shopping Mall

- [ ] Dough
- [ ] Bread
- [ ] A buck
- [ ] George Washington
- [ ] A piggy bank
- [ ] A "charge"
- [ ] Big "Bills"
- [ ] An ATM

Ice Rink

- [ ] A cool cat
- [ ] "Ice" spy
- [ ] A snowshoe
- [ ] A polar bear
- [ ] Cold cash
- [ ] A giant snowflake
- [ ] Cold feet
- [ ] A cold turkey

Zoo

- [ ] A rattlesnake
- [ ] A wolf in sheep's clothing
- [ ] An owl and a pussycat
- [ ] A big fish in a small pond
- [ ] A pack rat
- [ ] Birds of a feather
- [ ] Reigning cats and dogs
- [ ] Bats in the belfry

Trains

- ☐ John Henry and his hammer
- ☐ Railroad "tie"
- ☐ Hoboes
- ☐ A cow "catcher"
- ☐ A roundhouse
- ☐ An iron horse
- ☐ A golden spike

Gingerbread Factory

- ☐ A gingerbread igloo
- ☐ A gingerbread skyscraper
- ☐ A gingerbread tree house
- ☐ A gingerbread school
- ☐ A gingerbread museum
- ☐ A gingerbread fire station
- ☐ A gingerbread church
- ☐ A gingerbread bridge

Santa's Workshop

- ☐ An elf who has lost his marbles
- ☐ An elf who has flipped his lid
- ☐ An elf who's not all there
- ☐ An elf who has gone nuts
- ☐ An elf who is one brick short of a load
- ☐ An elf who has become cuckoo
- ☐ An elf who has a screw loose

School Party

- ☐ Class clown
- ☐ Teacher's pet
- ☐ Captain of the football team
- ☐ Prom queen
- ☐ Head cheerleader
- ☐ Reporter for the school newspaper
- ☐ Gym teacher
- ☐ Art teacher

House

- ☐ A night "mare"
- ☐ A "knight" club
- ☐ A night owl
- ☐ "Knight" fall
- ☐ Night school
- ☐ Florence Nightingale
- ☐ A dream boat
- ☐ A starfish
- ☐ A "moon" light

Santa

E veryone loves to decorate for Christmas! And of course, "yours truly" appears in many wonderful decorations. Check out this craft show — I'm a hot item this year! See if you can find me in all these crafts. Don't forget to find the real me, too!

2 Santa cookies

A Santa stocking

A Santa lamp

A Santa pillow

A wooden Santa doll

A Santa wreath

A Santa quilt

Santa in a centerpiece

How do I know not to bring you the same toys your parents are giving you? I visit toy stores and watch what people buy! Toy stores are almost as busy as my workshop at the North Pole — kids are always getting lost there. First, try to find me. Then see if you can find these lost children.

Bobby the Kid

Mini-Muscles, the Wonder Baby

Drummond Bugle III

I. Wright Ticketts

Lil' Topknot

Mona Lisa Murphy

Chuckles and Giggles, the twin clowns

Presto Change-o

Hi Long Leggs Jr.

MUSIC

FREE SET OF EARPLUGS WITH EVERY PURCHASE

One of my favorite things about Christmas is that I get to visit with girls and boys who come to see me at shopping malls. Shopping malls can be pretty crazy at Christmas, though! I'm taking a break right now. Can you find me? Can you find these crazy Christmas shoppers, too?

Curly Wiggs

Kringles the Klown

Tarzan

M.T. Pocketts

Mother Goose

Moe Hawk

Candi Cotton

Leif Eric's son

Christmas is only a few days away. And if you think it's busy at your house, you should see my workshop! Do you think I'll be ready for my Christmas Eve ride? After you find me, help me find these toys to fill my sack. We'd better check the list twice!

A ball

A red wagon

A train

A skateboard

A doll

A tricycle

A teddy bear

A truck

'Twas the night before Christmas,
    and all through these houses,
People were still up,
    including some mouses!

Well, this isn't *exactly* the way my
favorite poem goes, but my way is
more realistic! See if you can find
me, and then see if you can spot
these Christmas Eve classics.

A mouse
not stirring

4 children
nestled all snug
in their beds

This stocking
hung by the
chimney with care

Sugarplums
dancing

2 fathers in
sleeping caps

Cookies and milk
left out for me

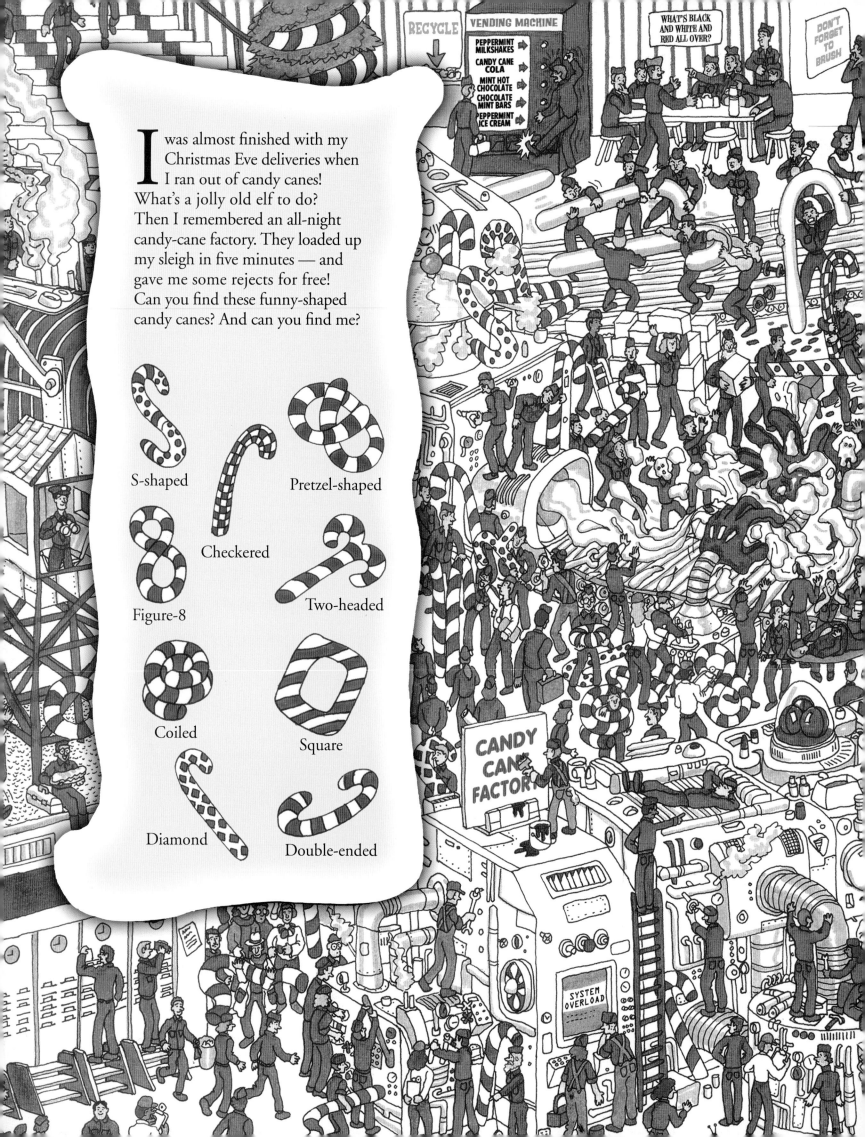

I was almost finished with my Christmas Eve deliveries when I ran out of candy canes! What's a jolly old elf to do? Then I remembered an all-night candy-cane factory. They loaded up my sleigh in five minutes — and gave me some rejects for free! Can you find these funny-shaped candy canes? And can you find me?

S-shaped

Pretzel-shaped

Checkered

Figure-8

Two-headed

Coiled

Square

Diamond

Double-ended

RECYCLE

VENDING MACHINE

PEPPERMINT MILKSHAKES

CANDY CANE COLA

MINT HOT CHOCOLATE

CHOCOLATE MINT BARS

PEPPERMINT ICE CREAM

WHAT'S BLACK AND WHITE AND RED ALL OVER?

DON'T FORGET TO BRUSH

CANDY CANE FACTORY

SYSTEM OVERLOAD

THE CHRISTMAS PARTY LINER

THE TINY TIM

Most people think I only fly through the air to deliver Christmas gifts. The mermaids, mermen, and other sea creatures will tell you differently. In fact, I swim so well, they think I'm one of them! Can you find me? Can you find this other silly sea stuff?

A Christmas seal

A hammerhead shark

All eight of my reindeer

An angelfish

A catfish

A peanut-butter-and-jellyfish

5 notes in a bottle

A submarine

TITANIC

DEAR SANDY CLAWS PLEASE GIVE ME A
1.
2.
3.

To: Long John Silver

I had "wrapped up" my Christmas Eve rounds when I realized I hadn't wrapped my gift to Mrs. Claus yet! I stopped at Worldwide Gift Wrap, Inc., to see if they could help me out. Boy, were they busy! I decided to wrap Mrs. Claus's fuzzy slippers myself. After you find me, see if you can find these things that will help me wrap my gift.

A green shoebox

A stapler

A red ruler

Candy-cane wrapping paper

A green tape dispenser

A snowman card

A pair of yellow scissors

A pencil

MODELS WANTED & TINY REINDEER

CARDS & TAGS DEPARTMENT

RIBBONS & BOWS DEPARTMENT

BOWS

MERRY CHRISTMAS

WORLDWIDE GIFT WRAP, INC.

GIFT WRAP WHILE-U-WAIT

SNACK BAR

BOSS'S OFFICE

BOX DEPARTMENT

PAPER-PRINTING PRESSES

Mrs. Claus thinks I've put on a little weight lately. She suggested I take up skiing and skating. The ski lessons were fun, but it went downhill after that! After you find me, see if you can find all of these other silly skiers and skaters.

A skier in a fur coat

A real cool dude

"Duck!"

Wroger Wrongway

Somebody who's all "wrapped up" in skiing

A skier who's "out of this world!"

A real rockin' skier

A figure skater

Go back to all the Santa scenes to find even more things!

Toy Store

- [ ] Bobby the Kid's dad
- [ ] Mini-Muscles's dad
- [ ] Drummond Bugle's dad
- [ ] I. Wright Ticketts's mom
- [ ] Lil' Topknot's mom
- [ ] Mona Lisa's dad
- [ ] Chuckles and Giggles's parents
- [ ] Presto's parents
- [ ] Hi Long Leggs's dad

Craft Show

- [ ] A runaway gingerbread man
- [ ] A "door" prize
- [ ] A pickpocket plant
- [ ] Paul Bunyan's mom
- [ ] A pig in a blanket
- [ ] Pinocchio
- [ ] A real fruit cake
- [ ] A vampire

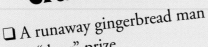

Shopping Mall

- [ ] A tortoise racing a hare
- [ ] Music soothing the savage beast
- [ ] A jealous musician
- [ ] An indoor snowfall
- [ ] Dorothy's slipper
- [ ] The Three Little Pigs
- [ ] A bunny wearing people slippers

Santa's Workshop

- [ ] A giant pan of Christmas cookies
- [ ] An elf tied to the train tracks
- [ ] A dog stealing a dolly
- [ ] A mouse running up a clock
- [ ] An elf who's the "target" of a prank
- [ ] A cowboy riding a reindeer
- [ ] A railroad "block"-ade

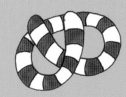

Houses

- ❑ Grandma
- ❑ A frantic dad
- ❑ A sudsy "Santa"
- ❑ A "cool" doghouse
- ❑ A cat burglar
- ❑ A snowman who's out of this world

Candy-Cane Factory

- ❑ A sweet snowman
- ❑ A candy-cane rapper
- ❑ A candy-cane napper
- ❑ A guy with ants in his pants
- ❑ A worker carried away by his job
- ❑ A worker whose bubble hasn't burst

The Ocean

- ❑ A sea horse race
- ❑ An oyster bed
- ❑ A "cave" with an appetite
- ❑ Three men in a tub
- ❑ A hotdog surfer
- ❑ A gold miner
- ❑ A school of fish

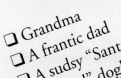

Worldwide Gift Wrap, Inc.

- ❑ A magic carpet
- ❑ Two boxers that are not people
- ❑ A Christmas "spirit"
- ❑ A swingin' monkey
- ❑ A pair of boxer shorts
- ❑ A very large gift with a trunk
- ❑ A boxed bicycle
- ❑ A "card" game

Ski Hill

- ❑ The Abominable Snowman
- ❑ A sunbather
- ❑ An angel
- ❑ The Easter Bunny
- ❑ A cowboy …
- ❑ … and his horse
- ❑ A hotdog skier
- ❑ A high chair

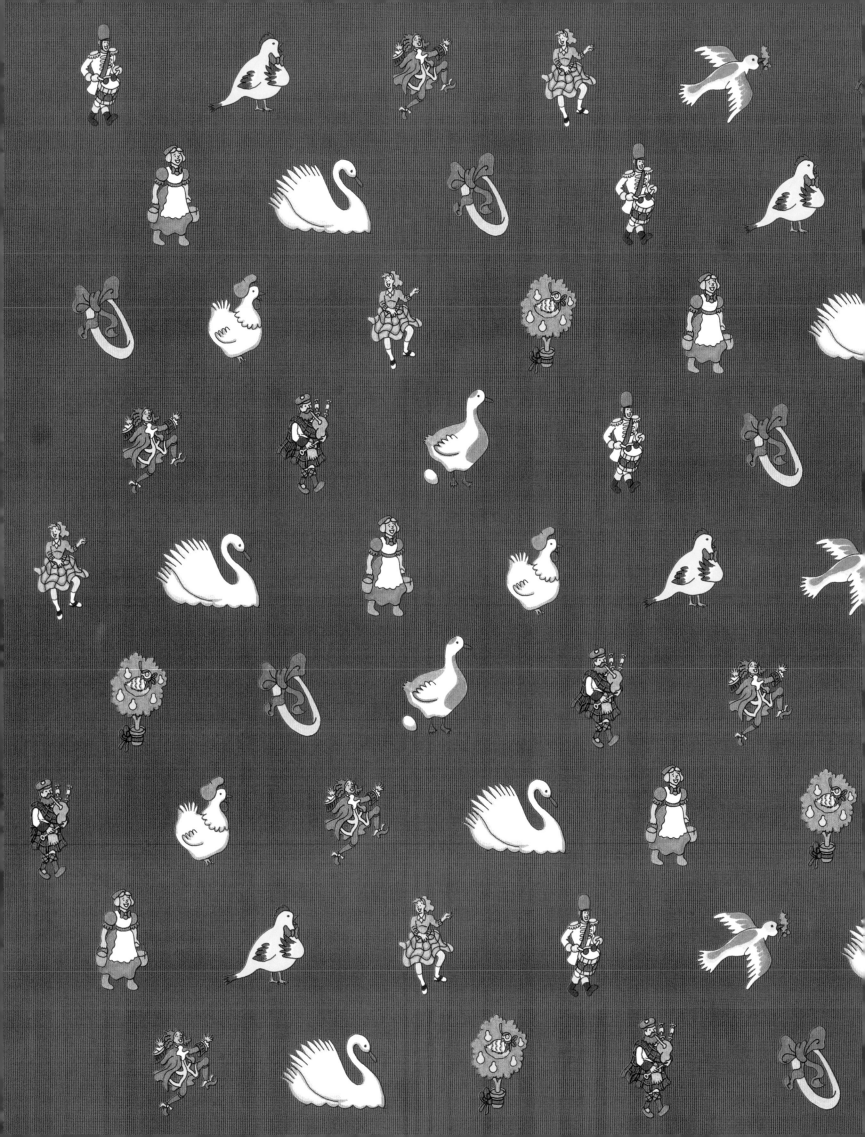

On the 1st day of Christmas
my true love sent to me
a partridge in a pear tree.

On the 2nd day of Christmas
my true love sent to me

2 turtle doves

& a partridge in a pear tree.

Kringle's Nursery was having a sale on
partridges in pear trees. But where do you
suppose my true love found two turtle
doves? (What is a turtle dove, anyway?)

MISTLETOE

BEAN STALK

PEPPERS

SALE

KRINGLE'S NURSERY

BUY YOUR
CHRISTMAS
PARTRIDGE
NOW!

PUMPKINS
$5.00
$3.00
$1.00
FREE!

FAMILY
TREE

On the **3rd** day of Christmas
my true love sent to me…

On the **4th** day of Christmas
my true love sent to me

4 calling birds,

3 French hens,

2 turtle doves,

& a partridge in a pear tree.

Birds, birds, and more birds! How
will I know which ones are from my
true love? And where will I put 10
birds and a pear tree?

On the **5th** day of Christmas my true love sent to me

5 golden rings,

4 calling birds,

3 French hens,

2 turtle doves,

& a partridge in a pear tree.

Things look pretty crazy at S. Claus & Sons Department Store! I hope my true love didn't have to wait in a long line to buy my five golden rings.

On the **6th** day of Christmas
my true love sent to me

6 geese a-laying,

5 golden rings,

4 calling birds,

3 French hens,

2 turtle doves,

& a partridge in a pear tree.

There's nothing like Christmas
down on the farm. It is so peaceful
and quiet. Or is it?

On the **7th** day of Christmas my true love sent to me

7 swans a-swimming,

6 geese a-laying,

5 golden rings,

4 calling birds,

3 French hens,

2 turtle doves,

& a partridge in a pear tree.

Christmas isn't all sleigh rides and snowflakes! In fact, my true love saw Santa playing a quick nine holes down in Florida this year!

On the **8th** day of Christmas
my true love sent to me

8   maids a-milking,

7   swans a-swimming,

6   geese a-laying,

5   golden rings,

4   calling birds,

3   French hens,

2   turtle doves,

&   a partridge in a pear tree.

Oh, my! What shall I do with all
this milk? I think I shall churn it
into butter and bake cookies.

On the **9th** day of Christmas my true love sent to me

9 ladies dancing,

8 maids a-milking,

7 swans a-swimming,

6 geese a-laying,

5 golden rings,

4 calling birds,

3 French hens,

2 turtle doves,

& a partridge in a pear tree.

My true love must have had to shop around the clock to find all these swell Christmas gifts!

GOOD FOOD

SODA SHOP
SODA   5¢
MILKSHAKES 10¢
BURGERS   20¢
FRIES   5¢
EXTRA GREASE 5¢

On the **10th** day of Christmas
my true love sent to me

10 lords a-leaping,

9 ladies dancing,

8 maids a-milking,

7 swans a-swimming,

6 geese a-laying,

5 golden rings,

4 calling birds,

3 French hens,

2 turtle doves,

& a partridge in a pear tree.

I'm going to need a bigger attic to
hold all these lords and ladies and
maids and...whew! My true love is
going completely overboard this year!

On the **11th** day of Christmas
my true love sent to me…

On the **12th** day of Christmas
my true love sent to me

12 drummers drumming,

11 pipers piping,

10 lords a-leaping,

9 ladies dancing,

8 maids a-milking,

7 swans a-swimming,

6 geese a-laying,

5 golden rings,

4 calling birds,

3 French hens,

2 turtle doves,

& a partridge in a pear tree.

Go back to all the Twelve Days of Christmas scenes to find even more things!

Kringle's Nursery

- [ ] Peter Piper and his peck of pickled peppers
- [ ] George and his cherry tree
- [ ] A lemon that is not a fruit
- [ ] Pretty powerful mistletoe
- [ ] Two squirrels who are nuts
- [ ] A family tree
- [ ] A pumpkinhead
- [ ] Eve and the apple
- [ ] A shoe tree

City Zoo Bird House

- [ ] "A bird in the hand is worth more than two in the bush"
- [ ] Jailbirds
- [ ] Two cans
- [ ] A proud peacock
- [ ] A birdbath
- [ ] Lovebirds
- [ ] An even balder eagle
- [ ] Blackbirds baked in a pie
- [ ] A rubber chicken

Candy Cane Farm

- [ ] The Ugly Duckling
- [ ] Baa, baa, black sheep
- [ ] The farmer in the dell
- [ ] Little Bo Peep
- [ ] The cow jumped over the moon
- [ ] Three Billy Goats Gruff
- [ ] Peter, Peter, pumpkin eater
- [ ] Three Little Pigs
- [ ] Little Miss Muffet
- [ ] Mary had a little lamb

S. Claus & Sons Department Store

- [ ] Long John Silver
- [ ] A peeping Tom
- [ ] A pampered pet
- [ ] A "pool" table
- [ ] A powerful vacuum cleaner
- [ ] A customer who is "all washed up"
- [ ] A sleeping beauty
- [ ] "Strike!"
- [ ] A pair of diamonds

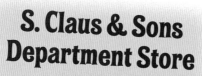

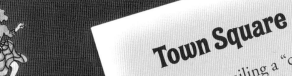
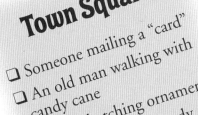

Golf Course

- ☐ Santa Claus and his reindeer
- ☐ A hole in 1
- ☐ A golfer who is "half in the bag"
- ☐ A hero
- ☐ A golfer choosing an "iron"
- ☐ A real handlebar mustache
- ☐ A golf T
- ☐ Love at first sight
- ☐ A flamingo wearing golf shoes
- ☐ A golfer yelling "FOUR!"

Town Square

- ☐ Someone mailing a "card"
- ☐ An old man walking with a candy cane
- ☐ A bird hatching ornaments
- ☐ A dog burying a candy cane
- ☐ An igloo
- ☐ A strange hockey stick
- ☐ A real stocking cap
- ☐ A sunbather
- ☐ A snow "cone" man

Soda Shop

- ☐ Two pairs of socks hopping
- ☐ A martian spaceship
- ☐ A hound dog
- ☐ A real beehive hairdo
- ☐ A poodle skirt barking back
- ☐ A customer in ice-cream shock
- ☐ Someone stepping on blue-suede shoes
- ☐ Santa Claus checking his menu
- ☐ Two bugs jitterbugging

Fancy Dress Ball

- ☐ Captain Hook
- ☐ Two ladies feeling a draft
- ☐ A guest who thinks the punch is too strong
- ☐ Rumpelstiltskin
- ☐ A guest dressed in fish
- ☐ Cinderella's glass slipper
- ☐ A joker making a real toast
- ☐ A princess kissing a frog
- ☐ The Tin Man

Christmas Parade

- ☐ A pied piper
- ☐ A scaredy-cat
- ☐ Three marching snowmen
- ☐ An elephant playing his trunk
- ☐ A skateboard "hotdogger"
- ☐ Beavers cutting a clown down to size
- ☐ A purple cow
- ☐ A marching cupcake
- ☐ Half of a horse

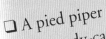